# Waterfalls

## IN ILLINOIS

**HIDDEN BEAUTY. NEAR YOUR DOORSTEP.**

**AN INTERPRETIVE GUIDE TO THE
GEOLOGICAL SIDE OF ILLINOIS WATERFALL WONDERS**

BY *Max W. Reams*
WITH *Carol A. Reams*

ISBN 9798642261156

Independently Published

Designed by Randall Rupert

Cover photo courtesy of Levi S. Gambill

## ACKNOWLEDGMENTS and DEDICATION

We are grateful to thoughtful and insightful readers. Their excellent suggestions, careful work, and attention to details greatly improved the text. All errors are the senior author's. The book is dedicated to our children, grandchildren, and great-grandchildren.

## ABOUT THE AUTHORS

Max W. Reams taught geology at Olivet Nazarene University for over five decades. His Ph.D. is from Washington University (St. Louis). His specializations include the study of caves and sedimentary rocks.

Carol A. Reams gathered field data, provided art critiques, and detailed editing. Her bachelors and master's degrees are from Olivet Nazarene University.

Other book titles: Geology of Illinois State Parks, Oil on My Hands (a detective novel), Before your Journey (a study guide for premarried couples), On the Journey (a study guide for married couples).

# TABLE of CONTENTS

# Getting Started

Waterfalls have fascinated humans for as long as our occupation on planet Earth. Artists, photographers, and travelers alike admire the beauty and mesmerizing effect of falling water. Cascades of foaming water create an aura of light and sound to soothe the mind and spirit. Sitting beside a waterfall allows us a visual and auditory release from the stresses of daily life. Residents of Illinois are privileged to enjoy many beautiful waterfalls in the Prairie State. Waterfalls are not restricted to mountains or far-off vistas. Long distance vacations are not necessary to find the sublime effects of water in free fall. Experience the beauty and calming effects of waterfalls which may be close to your home.

A companion to *Geology of Illinois State Parks* (Reams, 2013), this writing focuses on examples from Illinois' waterfall regions, with geological commentary about how these amazing features form and change. Keep both books in your vehicle while on a trip in Illinois. Take this book on walks through state parks or the Shawnee National Forest.

# What is a Waterfall?

Streams do not always flow smoothly. "White water" happens where rocks in a stream cause turbulence. Three natural features are classified as waterfalls (after Ford, 1968):

**Rapids:** If you see white water in a stream bed with rock but no change in a stream's slope, this is a *rapid* (Figure 1).

**Cascade:** If there are a succession of small falls or steps along a short section of a stream, this is a *cascade* (Figure 2).

**Waterfall:** If rock in the stream bed causes such a steep slope that water is in free fall, this is a *waterfall* (Figure 3).

# Visiting Illinois Waterfalls

Most waterfalls described in this book are in state parks or the Shawnee National Forest. All waterfalls are dangerous. *Never climb a waterfall* or risk life and limb trying to take the perfect photograph. Individuals are injured or die every year near Illinois waterfalls (Ross and Reams, 2015a, 2015b; Gambill et al., 2018). View waterfalls from a distance and *make safety your priority*. Snakes are common in rocky areas. Rocks on waterfalls are slippery. Stay away from cliff edges. Most Illinois waterfalls do *not* have protective fences. In winter, frozen waterfalls are beautiful, but trails are icy.

To view waterfalls requires walking or hiking over a variety of terrains. Roads can be smooth or potholed. Read travel notes, check current weather and road/trail conditions. Heed flash flood watches and warnings; flash floods are dangerous. During dry seasons, intermittent waterfalls may display little falling water.

*Never* visit a waterfall on private property without prior permission or a public park after closing hours. No responsibility is assumed by the author or publisher for accidents incurred as a result of visiting or attempting to visit a waterfall described herein. No claim is made for accuracies of locations, ownership, descriptions, dangers, or how to reach waterfalls. When visiting waterfalls, "Take nothing but pictures, leave nothing behind".

Soak in a waterfall's beauty. Meditate as splashing water releases stress. Absorb the serenity of falling water, rocks, and vegetation. Enjoy these amazing, unique, wonderful works of God!

Field data collected for this book involved an iPad for GPS locations, a Laser Atlanta Advantage® handheld rangefinder for estimating waterfall heights (± 1 to 2 ft), and information from printed, online, and park sources. Waterfall names follow nomenclature from the World Waterfall Database.

**Figure 1:** *Great Falls of the Illinois. Sandstone rapids.*

**Figure 2:** *French Canyon, Starved Rock State Park. A cascade on layers of Ordovician sandstone. Note box canyon with flat floor.*

**Figure 3:** *Cascade Falls, Matthiessen State Park. Vertical falling water is a waterfall (photo courtesy of Danielle Conrad).*

# Waterfalls and Rocks

Bedrock resistant to stream erosion is necessary to form waterfalls. There are three kinds of bedrock:

**Igneous** rocks were molten, then cooled to form solid rocks, e.g., granite and basalt. No igneous rocks form waterfalls in Illinois.

**Metamorphic** rocks form by deep burial and heating of other rocks, e.g., slate and gneiss. None are at the surface in Illinois.

**Sedimentary** rocks are cemented and compacted sediments, e.g., mud, sand, gravel, or shells. Illinois waterfalls are on these rocks:

*Sandstone* is sand buried in the Earth and cemented with minerals chemically deposited by water. Many sandstones resist weathering and erosion (Figure 4), but slowly break apart to form sand. Most Illinois waterfalls have resistant sandstone caprocks.

*Shale* is mud compacted during burial in the Earth to form a thinly layered mixture of clay and silt. Shale is the most erodible of common rocks. Where shale occurs below a resistant caprock, this combination is conducive to waterfall formation (Figure 5).

*Limestone* is ground up animal shells tossed by sea waves and cemented by minerals chemically deposited from water. Most shells are made of the mineral calcite. Limestones are less resistant to erosion than many sandstones, but more resistant than shales (Figure 5). Limestones form some waterfalls in Illinois.

*Dolostone* is limestone chemically altered by mineral-rich waters to form the mineral dolomite. Dolostones behave like limestone and form some waterfalls in Illinois (Figure 6).

Sedimentary rocks are arranged in layers, or strata (Figure 7). The order of stacking in flat-lying sedimentary strata is an important factor in Illinois waterfalls.

*Figure 4:*
Pennsylvanian sandstone, Shawnee National Forest. Vertical cracks are natural joints enlarged by weathering.

*Figure 5:*
Mississippian dark colored limestone overlying light-colored shale, near Vienna.

*Figure 6:*
Ordovician dolostone, Kankakee River State Park. Weathering along vertical fractures and bedding surfaces breaks rock into blocks.

*Figure 7:*
Mississippian strata near Vienna. Limestones form resistant ledges; vegetated, recessed layers are shales.

4. Sandstone

4. Limestone over Shale

4. Dolostone

4. Strata

Earth history is divided into time units called *Eras, Periods,* and *Epochs.*
**Figure 8** compiles these ages of rocks in Illinois. Refer to this figure when
periods of rocks are mentioned in the text.

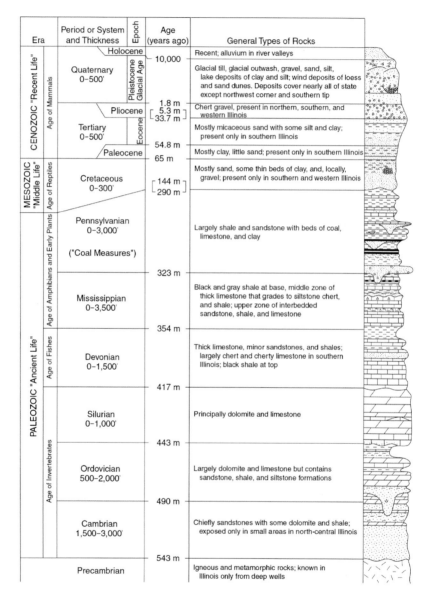

| Era | | Period or System and Thickness | Epoch | Age (years ago) | General Types of Rocks | |
|---|---|---|---|---|---|---|
| CENOZOIC "Recent Life" | Age of Mammals | | Holocene | 10,000 | Recent; alluvium in river valleys | |
| | | Quaternary 0–500' | Pleistocene Glacial Age | | Glacial till, glacial outwash, gravel, sand, silt, lake deposits of clay and silt; wind deposits of loess and sand dunes. Deposits cover nearly all of state except northwest corner and southern tip | |
| | | | Pliocene | 1.8 m, 5.3 m, 33.7 m | Chert gravel, present in northern, southern, and western Illinois | |
| | | Tertiary 0–500' | Eocene | 54.8 m | Mostly micaceous sand with some silt and clay; present only in southern Illinois | |
| | | | Paleocene | 65 m | Mostly clay, little sand; present only in southern Illinois | |
| MESOZOIC "Middle Life" | Age of Reptiles | Cretaceous 0–300' | | 144 m, 290 m | Mostly sand, some thin beds of clay, and, locally, gravel; present only in southern and western Illinois | |
| PALEOZOIC "Ancient Life" | Age of Amphibians and Early Plants | Pennsylvanian 0–3,000' ("Coal Measures") | | | Largely shale and sandstone with beds of coal, limestone, and clay | |
| | | | | 323 m | | |
| | Age of Fishes | Mississippian 0–3,500' | | | Black and gray shale at base, middle zone of thick limestone that grades to siltstone chert, and shale; upper zone of interbedded sandstone, shale, and limestone | |
| | | | | 354 m | | |
| | | Devonian 0–1,500' | | | Thick limestone, minor sandstones, and shales; largely chert and cherty limestone in southern Illinois; black shale at top | |
| | | | | 417 m | | |
| | Age of Invertebrates | Silurian 0–1,000' | | | Principally dolomite and limestone | |
| | | | | 443 m | | |
| | | Ordovician 500–2,000' | | | Largely dolomite and limestone but contains sandstone, shale, and siltstone formations | |
| | | | | 490 m | | |
| | | Cambrian 1,500–3,000' | | | Chiefly sandstones with some dolomite and shale; exposed only in small areas in north-central Illinois | |
| | | | | 543 m | | |
| | | Precambrian | | | Igneous and metamorphic rocks; known in Illinois only from deep wells | |

*Figure 8:* Generalized geologic column for rocks in Illinois. From Weibel and Nelson (2009).
Copyright © 2009 University of Illinois Board of Trustees.
Used with permission of the Illinois State Geological Survey.

**Figure 9** is a map of Illinois bedrock. Most older period rocks are covered with glacial deposits of the Pleistocene Epoch (a subdivision of the Quaternary Period).

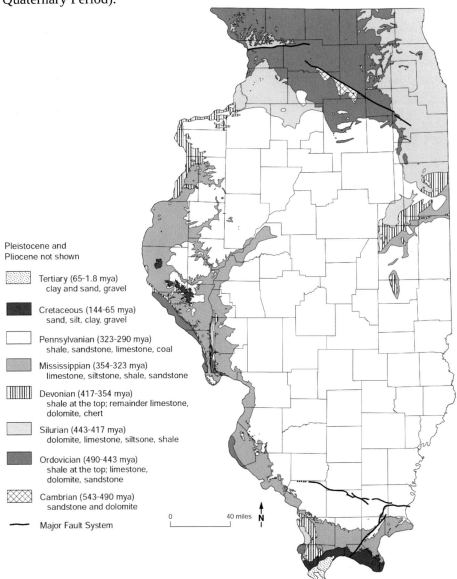

Pleistocene and
Pliocene not shown

Tertiary (65-1.8 mya)
clay and sand, gravel

Cretaceous (144-65 mya)
sand, silt, clay, gravel

Pennsylvanian (323-290 mya)
shale, sandstone, limestone, coal

Mississippian (354-323 mya)
limestone, siltstone, shale, sandstone

Devonian (417-354 mya)
shale at the top; remainder limestone,
dolomite, chert

Silurian (443-417 mya)
dolomite, limestone, siltsone, shale

Ordovician (490-443 mya)
shale at the top; limestone,
dolomite, sandstone

Cambrian (543-490 mya)
sandstone and dolomite

— Major Fault System

0        40 miles

N

*Figure 9: Bedrock geology beneath the surficial deposits in Illinois. From Weibel and Nelson (2009). Copyright © 2009 University of Illinois Board of Trustees. Used with permission of the Illinois State Geological Survey.*

# Geologic Setting

The oldest rocks in Illinois were formed during the Precambrian Era. These ancient rocks are buried under thousands of feet of Paleozoic Era sedimentary rocks throughout the state.

Paleozoic strata are divided into Periods and underlie most of Illinois (Figures 8 and 9). These rocks were deposited when Illinois was partly covered by shallow seawater. Most Illinois waterfalls form on these Paleozoic rocks: Pennsylvanian, Mississippian, Silurian, and Ordovician. Most scientific names for individual rock layers are omitted to reduce jargon in the text.

Mesozoic Era sedimentary rocks cover Paleozoic rocks in a few places (Figures 8 and 9). There are no Illinois Mesozoic rock waterfalls.

Cenozoic Era is mainly the Quaternary Period, especially the Pleistocene Epoch. Pleistocene ice sheets from Canada spread south, past Carbondale, leaving deposits called till. Glaciers touched all of Illinois except parts of the northwest, west-central, and southern tip. Glaciers melted and released huge quantities of meltwater that eroded through till and bedrock. This triggered the formation of many Illinois waterfalls on Paleozoic rocks.

# How Waterfalls Begin

All waterfalls begin at knickpoints, geological events or rock characteristics that cause sharp increases in stream channel slopes. Not all knickpoints display waterfalls. Just the right strata are needed. Falling water and other processes erode rocks so waterfalls migrate upstream, called waterfall retreat. Examples are drawn from Illinois' four main waterfall areas:

- The Illinois River Valley

- The Kankakee River Valley

- The Southern Illinois Caseyville Escarpment

- The Mississippi River Bluffs.

# Illinois River Valley
## Starved Rock State Park

**Travel to Park:** From I-80 Exit 81: Drive south on IL-178 to Starved Rock State Park. All waterfalls are marked on trail map available online or at Visitor Center. Waterfalls are accessible from Visitor Center, Lodge, or parking lots at west end off IL-178 and lots off IL-71 east of park entrance. Walking trails follow either bluffs or the river level. Ask for directions at Visitor Center.

**Safety in the Park:** You might check with a physician about climbing up and down steep stairs and taking vigorous hikes. Many staircases connect high cliffs with the river walk. Terrain is uneven. Inquire at Visitor Center about trail difficulty and access. Carry water and a map. Traveling with a companion is safer.

Starved Rock is perhaps the most beautiful and *dangerous* Illinois state park. Falling off sheer cliffs has injured and killed unwary visitors. Guard rails exist only in some places. Watch children closely. Parks are chosen for beauty, not safety. Rock climbing is illegal at Starved Rock. This is due to loose sand on rocks (Figure 12). Never climb any waterfall. Algae and wet slippery rocks are often one's undoing. Stay on trails. Expect large amounts of loose and deep sand on trails near a waterfall. Watch for ice in winter.

# How Starved Rock waterfalls began

Toward the end of Pleistocene ice ages, vast glaciers from Canada were melting away. As a result, huge amounts of meltwater raced past Kankakee and rushed into the Illinois River Valley. Fast moving water carved out bedrock from the Illinois River bed. This occurred in a series of events called the Kankakee Torrent or Flood between about 18,000 to 18,900 years ago (Curry et al., 2014). Floods scoured the river channel and removed Paleozoic rocks down into the Ordovician St. Peter Sandstone. Erosion 14,000 to 15,000 years ago by waters pouring out of an ancient lake near Chicago (Curry et al., 2014; Bruegger, A. R., 2016) exposed the sandstone bluffs seen today (Figure 10).

Small tributary streams that flowed into the Illinois River valley easily cut through glacial till and weak Pennsylvanian shale, sandstone, and coal beds. Downcutting by these streams slowed when they reached the Ordovician sandstone, which is more resistant than overlying strata (Figure 11).

Waterfalls started at knickpoints, where tributary streams reached Illinois River bluffs. Waterfalls began receding when the Illinois River level approached its current position 14,000 to 15,000 years ago. Park waterfalls are only in Ordovician sandstone, since this is the rock layer above the Illinois River (Figure 10).

The amount of water flowing in these tributaries depends on the size of the drainage basin. Large basins receive more rain and snow than small basins. Precipitation varies with seasons. Wet springs yield larger waterfall flow than dry summers.

*Figure 10 (left): Bluff of Ordovician St. Peter Sandstone on the Illinois River, Starved Rock State Park.*

*Figure 11 (right): Easily eroded dark Pennsylvanian shale and coal over resistant yellow Ordovician St. Peter Sandstone, Buffalo Rock State Park.*

*References: Irvine, 2001; Time Talks, 2005; Thomason, 2003.*

# How Starved Rock Park Waterfalls Retreat with Time

The sandstone is made of weakly cemented quartz grains (Figure 12). Rain falls on a drainage basin and seeps into rock. Groundwater flows to easy outlets, porous, poorly-cemented layers below well-cemented, less porous caprocks (Figure 13). Groundwater has three functions in sandstone waterfall retreat:

1. Water dissolves cement, which loosens sand grains.

2. Water exerts pressure, pushing grains and slabs off rock faces.

3. Water freezes and expands within pores and cracks in winter and pushes grains and slabs (Figure 14).

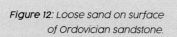

*Figure 12: Loose sand on surface of Ordovician sandstone.*

*Figure 13: Idealized groundwater flow in Starved Rock waterfalls. Groundwater seeks the easiest outlet: the poorly-cemented, more porous sandstone under the well-cemented, less porous caprock.*

**Resistant caprock sandstone**

**Groundwater flow**

**Porous sandstone**

*Figure 14: Slabs and sand grains fall from Ottawa Canyon alcove.*

These processes, also known as seepage erosion, act on waterfall rocks. Ledges mark resistant sandstones. Recessed alcoves form where seepage water exits from poorly-cemented sandstones (Figure 2). Falling water from a caprock washes loose sand downstream (Figure 15). During high flow, loose sand removal is accelerated. Seepage erosion is not limited to the underside of a waterfall. Groundwater seeps through sandstone bedrock in valley bluffs left by a retreating waterfall causing sand grains and blocks to fall to the valley floor (Figure 16). They, in turn, are washed downstream by floods. Seepage erosion acting on bluffs widens a valley.

Waterfall retreat and valley widening by seepage erosion produces a box canyon with an amphitheater waterfall face (Figure 3). These canyons mimic box canyons in the southwestern United States. Irvine (2001) verified these processes at Starved Rock.

Figure 15: *LaSalle Canyon Falls washes sand downstream.*

Figure 16: *Seepage erosion and freezing water likely caused this sandstone mass to fall, widening Kaskaskia's box canyon.*

41.3112, -88.9707

LaSalle Canyon Creek

*Travel:* Shortest access is from Parkman's Plain off IL-71, then descend the staircase. Long walks from Visitor's Center or Lodge.

# LaSalle Canyon Falls

LaSalle Canyon waterfall is a beautiful example of seepage erosion. Waterfall retreat is illustrated by collapse of sand masses from a waterfall alcove by groundwater seepage (Figure 17). The waterfall consists of a cascade, then the main waterfall drop 23.5 feet, more cascades, and a final waterfall drop of 4.5 feet into a plunge pool. Total drop from the upper cascade to the lowest plunge pool is 50 feet. The canyon head is an amphitheater shape. Sand at the base of bluffs is by seepage erosion along weak zones. This removal of bluff rock widens the canyon downstream and contributes to the box canyon appearance (Figure 18).

**Figure 17:** LaSalle Canyon Falls. Sandstone mass fell due to seepage erosion from alcove under the waterfall.

**Figure 18:** LaSalle Canyon Falls.

41.3189, -89.0056

St. Louis Canyon Creek

## St. Louis Canyon Falls

*Travel:* Take St. Louis Canyon Trail from Lodge or Visitor Center or from west end of Park in lot adjacent to IL-178.

This waterfall drops 58 feet to display an amphitheater with alternating alcoves and resistant sandstone layers (Figure 19). Seepage erosion is responsible for retreat of the waterfall and the box canyon, which widens with sandstone collapse (Figure 20).

**Figure 20**: St. Louis Canyon bluff with collapsed blocks and sand.

**Figure 19**: St. Louis Canyon Falls, winter. Courtesy of Bill Burger.

41.3163, -88.9833

Wildcat Canyon Creek

# Wildcat Canyon Falls

*Travel:* Take trails from Lodge or Visitor's Center.

Wildcat Falls displays an amphitheater, box canyon of steep canyon walls with alternating ledges and alcoves of sandstone, and a flat floor. All this is strong evidence of seepage erosion. Groundwater moves through poorly-cemented sandstones sandwiched between well-cemented layers. The 86-foot series of drops is breathtaking. The largest drop is 58 feet (Figure 21). Be careful taking photos.

*Figure 21.* Wildcat Canyon Falls.

*Figure 22.* Wildcat Canyon Falls. Flat floor and horseshoe canyon shape.

41.3065, -88.9471

Ottowa Canyon Creek

**Travel:** *Ottawa Canyon trail from lot on south side of IL-71.*

# Ottawa Canyon Falls

Ottawa Canyon waterfall height is 46 feet (Irvine, 2001). This waterfall illustrates how seepage erosion under resistant caprock causes waterfall retreat. Standing under the waterfall alcove during a moist season, one experiences a "rain" of small sand masses visibly and audibly falling from the alcove ceiling (Figure 23). Photos in Figure 24 taken 40 years apart illustrate this process by alcove color density changes. Loose sand and blocks fell from the alcove by seepage erosion loosening sand grains (Figure 14).

The waterfall retreated 472 feet from the Illinois River bluff (Irvine, 2001) over the past 14,000 to 15,000 years, which equals 0.0315 - 0.0337 ft./year (about 0.39 in./year). Irvine measured 0.036 ft./year (0.43 in./year). These data suggest the waterfall should have receded 1.26 to 1.51 feet in the 40 years between photos. Not so much. Did the waterfall retreat faster in the past? Perhaps the retreat rates are episodic.

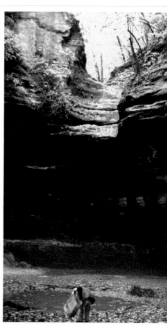

**Figure 23:** *Sand falls from Ottawa Canyon Falls alcove*

**Figure 24:** *Ottawa Canyon Falls.* **Above:** *October, 1974.* **Right:** *September, 2014*

*41.3171, -88.9916*

💧 *French Canyon Creek*

# French Canyon Falls

***Travel:*** *Lodge trail to top or Visitor's Center trail to stream level.*

French Canyon is the most visited Park canyon with easy access from the Visitor's Center. The waterfall is unique with a 30 - 35° inclined cascade of 48 feet (Irvine, 2001; Sauer, 1918) (Figure 2). Most Starved Rock waterfalls have vertical drops. Downstream from the cascade, the flat box canyon floor changes to a V-profile before switching back to a small cascade with plunge pool (Figure 25). Further downstream, the canyon widens to a box canyon before switching to another V-profile canyon (Figure 26). This going back and forth from box canyon to V-profiles is unusual for Starved Rock. V-profiles characterize non-seepage erosion streams. Box canyons form by seepage erosion. Irvine (2001) thought changes were due to hydrology variations during waterfall retreat. Alcoves indicate seepage erosion in poorly-cemented layers, but alcoves are small, suggesting sandstone layers have different porosities than other canyons. Perhaps non-uniform cementation is responsible for variations between Starved Rock waterfalls.

**Figure 25.** *French Canyon. V-profile looking upstream from lower cascade.*

**Figure 26:** *French Canyon. Downstream from lower cascade to box canyon profile followed by a second V-profile.*

41.3003, -88.9462

*Kaskaskia Canyon Creek*

# Kaskaskia Canyon Falls

**Travel**: *Take Kaskaskia Canyon trail from south side of IL-71 lot.*

This small waterfall in a deep canyon drops about 10 feet (Irvine, 2001). An alcove under an overhanging resistant sandstone layer suggests waterfall retreat by seepage erosion (Figure 27). The amphitheater waterfall area and box canyon are further evidences of seepage erosion (Figure 28). Large sandstone masses fall from steep bluffs and shatter on the box canyon floor (Figure 14). This is also due to seepage erosion. Groundwater dissolves cement and pushes grains and masses of sandstone away from cliffs. Winter freezes accelerate collapses. These processes widen the box canyon.

*Figure 27: Kaskaskia Canyon Falls. Alcove under caprock suggests seepage erosion through poorly-cemented sandstone.*

*Figure 28: Kaskaskia Canyon Falls. Example of collapse of canyon walls by seepage erosion forming arches as canyons are widened.*

41.3072, -88.9381

 Illinois Canyon Creek

**Travel:** Take Illinois Canyon trail from south side of IL-71 lot. Be aware that there is no developed trail.

**Safety Note:** Conditions are slippery. To reach the waterfall is dangerous. The stream must be crossed multiple times. Not recommended, especially for children.

# Illinois Canyon Falls

Illinois Canyon is the longest canyon in the Park. The waterfall height may be 10 feet. During high rainfall, other small waterfalls drop from canyon walls (Irvine, 2001). Seepage erosion by groundwater dissolves cement and pushes rock masses (Figure 29). Freezing aids box canyon widening.

**Figure 29:** Illinois Canyon. Sandstone blocks and loose sand fell from canyon walls by seepage erosion, widening the box canyon.

# Tonti Canyon Falls

41.3119, -88.9737

Tonti Canyon Creek

Tonti Canyon displays two separate waterfalls, each with plunge pools (Figure 30 shows one of the waterfalls). Irvine (2001) listed heights of 43 and 53 feet. Twin waterfalls are on separate joints (vertical fractures). Alcoves suggest seepage erosion.

**Travel**: See Visitor's Center for trail closures. Must cross stream.

**Figure 30:** Tonti Canyon Falls, winter. Flat vertical surface is a joint.

41.3125, -88.9651

 *Owl Canyon Creek*

*Travel: See Visitor's Center for a variety of trails.*

# Owl Canyon Falls

Height from waterfall lip to creek level is about 46 feet. The waterfall face is nearly vertical with some alcove development beneath resistant layers. Box canyon shape and abundant sand buildup under a seepage line are evidences supporting seepage erosion (Irvine, 2001).

 41.3184, -88.9970

 *Aurora Canyon Creek*

 41.3186, -88.9980

 *Sac Canyon Creek*

*Travel to Aurora and Sac:*
*St. Louis Canyon trail from Lodge, Visitor's Center, or IL-178 parking lot.*

# Aurora Canyon Falls & Sac Canyon Falls

These falls display cascades and small free drops. The total drops and cascades of Aurora Falls may be 80 feet; Sac Falls: perhaps 75 feet. Unlike other Park valleys, Aurora and Sac do not display box canyons, probably due to their small drainage basins. Small alcoves suggest possible seepage erosion by groundwater.

 41.3171, -88.9916

 *Fox Canyon Creek*

*Travel: Park in Starved Rock Lodge lot and walk toward Lodge. View waterfall canyon from the bridge to Lodge dropoff.*

# Fox Canyon Falls

Fox Canyon Falls is inaccessible except to view from the bridge. Irvine (2001) indicated a total drop of cascades and free drops of about 53 feet. A box canyon profile and amphitheater shape can be seen. Several resistant sandstone layers and underlying alcoves are visible from the bridge, suggesting seepage erosion.

# Illinois River Valley

## Matthiessen State Park (pronounced: math-eh-son)

**Travel:** From I-80 Exit 81: Drive south on IL-178; pass through North Utica; cross the Illinois River; continue past the intersection with IL-71 over a mile and turn right (west) at main entrance sign. Park in lot by restrooms. Walk down long stairs to bridge over Cascade Falls. Upper Dells is upstream to the right. Lower Dells, to the left, reaches the Vermillion River. See the trails map for details.

**Safety in the Park:** Be aware of a steep climb in and out of the gorge. The bridge can be muddy. Other dangers include floods, slippery steps, steep slopes, and cliffs. **Do not climb waterfalls.**

*Figure 31: Cascade Falls. Photo courtesy of Danielle Conrad.*

Matthiessen State Park waterfalls are tied to events forming Starved Rock waterfalls. Erosion by multiple glacial meltwater floods deepened the Illinois River (Kankakee Flood: 18,000 to 18,900 years; draining of an ancient lake near Chicago: 14,000 to 15,000 years) (Curry, et al, 2014; Bruegger, A. R., 2016). This also allowed downcutting of the Vermillion River, an Illinois River tributary. Vermillion valley erosion triggered a knickpoint where Deer Park Creek, a Vermillion tributary, entered. Hills are capped by easily eroded glacial till, Pennsylvanian limestone, shale, sandstone, and coal, and Ordovician limestone and dolostone. Deer Park Creek made quick work of these layers but slowed on reaching resistant Ordovician St. Peter Sandstone. This rock forms Cascade Falls, which has retreated from the knickpoint 2,000 feet in 14,000-15,000 years (1.65 in./year).

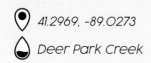

41.2969, -89.0273

Deer Park Creek

*Travel: View falls from the bridge or take Lower Dells trail (left) to a staircase to view falls from downstream.*

## Cascade Falls (Bridal Veil Falls)

Deer Park Creek's multi-tiered Cascade Falls on Ordovician sandstone is picturesque. Drops of 11, 5.5, and 39 feet lead to a rock surface that splashes into a plunge pool (Figures 3, 31, and 32). Total height from top waterfall to pool is 56 feet. The alcove below the caprock suggests seepage erosion. Groundwater moves through poorly-cemented sandstone below the caprock of more resistant rock, dissolving cement holding grains together. Water pressure pushes grains from the headwall. Downstream is a box canyon (Figure 32).

*Figure 32: Cascade Falls. View of box canyon from bridge.*

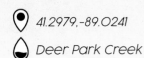

41.2979,-89.0241

*Deer Park Creek*

**Travel:** *Follow Bluff Trail upstream (right) from Cascade Falls bridge, descend stairs, and cross stream.*

**Safety Note:** *Proper footwear recommended.*

# Giant's Bathtub Falls & upper waterfall

Giant's Bathtub consists of drops, cascades, and plunge pool totaling 10.5 feet (Figure 33). Alcoves suggest seepage erosion.

At the stream's valley head is a human-altered waterfall of sandstone capped by Pennsylvanian strata (Figure 34). The erosion break between Ordovician St. Peter Sandstone and Pennsylvanian rocks is due to geologic uplift of Earth's crust. This deformed rock structure is called the LaSalle Anticline (Figure 35). Erosion of possible Devonian and Silurian was followed by deposition of Pennsylvanian rocks on eroded older Ordovician rocks.

**Figure 33**: *Giant's Bathtub plunge pool. Resistant and weak sandstones alternate. Photo courtesy of Danielle Conrad.*

*Figure 34: Canyon head waterfall. St. Peter Sandstone is capped by Pennsylvanian strata. Waterfall is modified by human activity. Photo courtesy of Danielle Conrad.*

*Figure 35: La Salle Anticline structure was uplifted during Early Pennsylvanian time. As uplift occurred, various strata were eroded. This caused a time break between older Periods and later Pennsylvanian rocks deposited on top.*

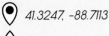

41.3247, -88.7113

Illinois River

*Travel from I-80 exit 97:*
*Drive south to parking lot at south edge of Marseilles by the Illinois River. View from a parking lot.*

# Outside Starved Rock and Matthiessen State Parks
### Great Falls of the Illinois

This is not a waterfall, but rapids (Figure 1). A resistant layer of Pennsylvanian sandstone forms the "Falls". This impeded river travel before locks, dams, and a bypass channel were constructed.

*Reference: Reinertsen, et al., 1992.*

# Kankakee River Valley

Glaciers were melting back near the end of Pleistocene Ice Ages. Three glaciers were arranged around a corridor stretching from northwest Indiana into northeast Illinois. This avenue was exit for glacial meltwaters that drained to the west. This water covered much of Kankakee county as the Kankakee Flood. The waters were so powerful they transported dolostone blocks two feet in diameter and scoured the Kankakee River valley. This lowered river level and triggered the formation of knickpoints on tributaries entering the Kankakee River. Some produced waterfalls on Silurian dolostone bedrock. Waterfall retreat began once floods ceased about 18,000 years ago.

**Figure 36:** Retreating Rock Creek Falls, Kankakee River State Park

References:
Frankie, 1997;
Curry et al., 2014

# How Kankakee River Valley Waterfalls Retreat

Silurian dolostone bedrock is not made of sand grains as seen in Starved Rock and Matthiessen State Parks. Dolostones are dense blocks arranged in layers of variable thickness. The shapes of blocks are controlled by horizontal beds broken with vertical joints. Bedrock exposures resemble bricks or concrete blocks.

Dolostone is made of dolomite, an easily dissolved mineral. Caves in bedrock are dissolved as water moves along joints and bedding surfaces. Dolostone blocks at waterfalls are eroded in four ways:

Stream water flows rapidly over upper surfaces of bedrock exposed at the waterfall.

Water from streams and surrounding watersheds seeps around blocks, dissolving the rock and opening spaces between blocks.

Pressure from turbulent water flowing over a waterfall pushes blocks, dislodges them, and transports rocks downstream.

During extreme cold snaps, water freezes around blocks, pushing them apart. This helps flowing water dislodge blocks.

These processes produce a stepped waterfall cascade, with no plunge pool. The waterfall front is sloped, with no vertical drop as in most sandstone waterfalls. The waterfall steps appearance depends on block sizes and the basin feeding water to a waterfall.

Dolostone waterfall retreat canyons differ from sandstone canyons in Starved Rock and Matthiessen State Parks. Dolostone canyons have no amphitheater and, contrary to sandstone waterfalls, the waterfall slopes are reduced as they retreat. Cascades degenerate into rapids and then disappear, although the 18,000-year-old Kankakee waterfalls have not progressed this far.

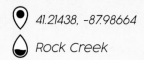

**Travel:** *Enter north entrance to Park off IL-102. Park in lot by Waterfall Trail sign. Walk ¾ mile to waterfall lookout.*

**Safety Note:**
*Creek wading is popular, but sinkholes and creek irregularities can be dangerous. Waders may encounter leeches. Waterfalls are slippery and should be avoided. Snakes are common. Monitor children. Avoid cliffs.*

# Kankakee River State Park
## Rock Creek Falls

This cascade on Silurian dolostone descends four feet via many steps and has no plunge pool. Rock Creek's large drainage basin provides greater water flow than most Illinois waterfalls. The Falls location is controlled by vertical fractures (joints) in dolostone bedrock as shown in Figure 37:

**Joint 1:** Fracture in bedrock extends from stream valley out into the stream bed underwater. The stream bank parallels the joint.

**Joint 2:** Fracture forms a vertical cliff face just upstream and to the right of Joint #1. Both joints are parallel to each other.

**Joint 3:** Fracture in rock at cliff edge and parallels Joints 1 and 2.

Joints are zones of weakness which water follows and enlarges as the stream erodes through bedrock. Notice the surface of the block of cliff bedrock between Joints 1 and 2. It looks identical to the present waterfall with a series of steps made of dolostone layers. This block represents the location of the waterfall many years ago. As the stream eroded bedrock, water flow shifted to an easier route, following joints to the right. Dolostone block surfaces are avenues for water to seep into and dissolve rock. Freezing of water expands and further separates blocks. Rushing water pushes against blocks and moves them downstream. These processes cause waterfall retreat. The cascade slope descends ±15 degrees on dolostone steps (Figure 38).

**Figure 37**: Rock Creek Falls

EARLIER WATERFALL LOCATION

JOINT 3

JOINT 1

JOINT 2

BEDROCK STAIRSTEPS

STAIRSTEP WATERFALL CASCADE

**Figure 38**: Rock Creek Falls.Sloping dolostone cascade.

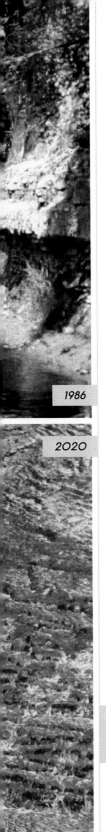

1986

2020

# How fast does Rock Creek Falls retreat?

Compare the location of the black hole at the base of the waterfall in both photographs (Figure 39), taken 34 years apart. The waterfall has retreated ¾ mile in 18,000 years since the Kankakee Flood subsided. If waterfall retreat has been constant, the Falls should have moved 7 feet in 34 years. However, the waterfall has barely moved. Perhaps the erosion rate was faster when the waterfall was tens of feet higher.

As Rock Creek Falls retreats, its slope and height are reduced (Gardner, 1983). After 18,000 years, the waterfall height has decreased about 40 feet. The average rate of retreat is 2.64 inches per year while the lowering rate is 0.027 inches per year. The waterfall retreats almost 100 times faster than waterfall height. This matches the observation that the present waterfall height is almost unchanged while retreating from the old waterfall surface block (Figure 37).

Irvine (2001) measured average Starved Rock waterfall retreats of about 0.79 inches per year. This is less than ⅓ the rate for Rock Creek's waterfall retreat. Starved Rock waterfalls retreat mainly by seepage erosion of porous sandstone. Rock Creek retreats by very different mechanisms of solution and mechanical pushing of dense dolostone blocks. Also, Rock Creek's larger watershed basin provides greater flows of water.

Historical photographs of Ottawa Canyon Falls in Starved Rock State Park and Rock Creek Falls both suggest that neither waterfall is retreating at calculated rates! Erosion rates seem to have decreased with time, perhaps for different reasons.

*Figure 39*: Rock Creek Falls.
34 years' time lapse between photos.

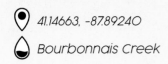

41.14663, -87.89240

Bourbonnais Creek

*Travel from I-57 exit 315:*
*Drive south on IL-50; turn*
*right (west) on Armour*
*Road; turn right onto*
*Canterbury Lane; go one*
*block, turn left on Bristol*
*Drive which curves at*
*right angle onto Percy*
*Drive; enter Cavalier de*
*LaSalle Park; park in*
*lot. Follow path to river*
*and go left until crossing*
*bridge over Bourbonnais*
*Creek. These are the*
*"Indian Caves"; turn left*
*after crossing bridge to*
*falls.*

*Safety Note: Watch*
*children. Bluffs are steep.*
*Don't wade toward*
*river due to a sinkhole*
*in stream bed. People*
*have died at both places.*
*BOurbonnais Creek's*
*easy upstream access*
*enhances popularity.*
*The creek bed is rough*
*and flash floods occur.*
*Waterfalls and bluffs are*
*slippery and best viewed*
*at a distance.*

# Outside Kankakee River State Park
## Bourbonnais Creek Waterfall

Bourbonnais Creek is a small tributary to the Kankakee River upstream from Kankakee River State Park. A small basin provides flow to Bourbonnais Creek. Bedrock Silurian dolostone is similar to Rock Creek's bedrock. However, Bourbonnais Creek's stream bed is stepped to make one long series of cascades (Figure 40). The Creek's position is controlled by joints, similar to Rock Creek. The stream zigs and zags as it follows cracks in bedrock.

*Figure 40: Bourbonnais Creek stepped cascades.*

With low flow, the knickpoint at the river has receded perhaps 200 feet, compared to Rock Creek's ¾ mile in 18,000 years. The result is a stepped steep-walled gorge leading to the valley bluff. Most of Bourbonnais Creek's energy is spent cutting a canyon, not on knickpoint waterfall retreat.

# Southern Illinois Caseyville Escarpment

The Caseyville Escarpment is a steep cliff of Pennsylvanian sandstones that extends east-west across southern Illinois. These rocks are more resistant to erosion than rocks to the north and south (Figures 41 and 42).

*Figure 41*: Interstate 24 roadcut through Caseyville Escarpment exposes Pennsylvanian sandstones and weak, underlying shale

GLACIAL TILL

CASEYVILLE ESCARPMENT
PENNSYLVANIAN SANDSTONES

WEAK PENNSYLVANIAN SEDIMENTARY ROCKS

*Figure 42*: Generalized geologic sketch map of the southern tip of Illinois (data from Kolata et al., 2005; and other sources).

WEAK MISSISSIPPIAN SEDIMENTARY ROCKS

Streams on Caseyville sandstones generally flow south or north, away from the highlands. Where these streams erode through resistant sandstone and expose weak shale below, the possibility for waterfalls exists. Shale erodes faster than sandstone.

# How do Southern Illinois Caseyville waterfalls retreat?

Knickpoints in southern Illinois start when a stream erodes through resistant Caseyville sandstone and exposes underlying weak shale. Once falling water washes out weak shale beneath the sandstone, a waterfall is established, similar to Niagara Falls in New York and Canada (Figure 43). Plunge pool turbulence erodes shale under the caprock. Once shale is washed away, sandstone blocks break off and the waterfall recedes (Figure 44).

This mechanism of waterfall retreat continues as long as shale is exposed to stream erosion. All streams slope downstream. So, as a waterfall retreats upstream, it migrates uphill. Eventually, the stream bed no longer runs on shale but on sandstone (Figure 45). Then, Niagara-style waterfall retreat shifts to seepage erosion waterfall retreat. Groundwater moves through porous, poorly-cemented sandstone layers below well-cemented, less porous sandstone caprock. This mimics seepage erosion seen in waterfalls of Starved Rock and Matthiessen State Parks. Groundwater dissolves cement that holds sand grains together. Water pressure pushes grains and slabs of sandstone away from under the caprock (Figure 48). Freezing in winter accelerates the process. Groundwater seeping through porous sandstone comes from precipitation on the drainage basin.

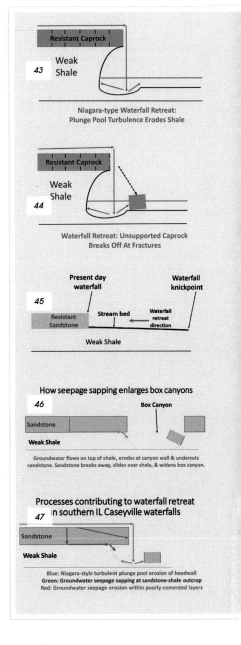

**43** Resistant Caprock / Weak Shale

Niagara-type Waterfall Retreat:
Plunge Pool Turbulence Erodes Shale

**44** Resistant Caprock / Weak Shale

Waterfall Retreat: Unsupported Caprock
Breaks Off At Fractures

**45** Present day waterfall — Waterfall knickpoint — Resistant Sandstone — Stream bed — Waterfall retreat direction — Weak Shale

How seepage sapping enlarges box canyons

**46** Box Canyon — Sandstone — Weak Shale

Groundwater flows on top of shale, erodes at canyon wall & undercuts sandstone. Sandstone breaks away, slides over shale, & widens box canyon.

Processes contributing to waterfall retreat in southern IL Caseyville waterfalls

**47** Sandstone — Weak Shale

Blue: Niagara-style turbulent plunge pool erosion of headwall
Green: Groundwater seepage sapping at sandstone-shale outcrop
Red: Groundwater seepage erosion within poorly-cemented layers

# How they retreat (CONTINUED)

Box canyons of southern Illinois differ from those in Starved Rock and Matthiessen State Parks in how they form. Groundwater seeping through sandstones in southern canyon bluffs reaches the impermeable shale. Water moves along the sandstone-shale boundary until it reaches canyon walls. Here, seepage washes away weak shale and undermines sandstone. Unsupported sandstone breaks off and slides downhill on wet shale. This seepage sapping widens valleys to form box canyons (Figure 46) and amphitheaters, as in the southwestern United States.

Seepage erosion and seepage sapping probably occur throughout the life of a southern Illinois waterfall. However, they are minor contributors to waterfall retreat as long as shale is eroded under sandstone (Figure 48). Seepage erosion is the main theme when no shale is eroded by falling water and erosion is in sandstone.

*Figure 48: Bork's Falls. Slabs collapse by seepage erosion.*

37.5416, -89.0211

Regent Creek

# Ferne Clyffe State Park
## Bork's Falls
### (Cave Falls; Regent Falls)

**Travel from I-24 Exit 7:**
Drive west to IL-37, turn right (north to Goreville; turn left (west) on Goreville Road; turn left (south) on Regent Lane (2.5 miles west of Goreville).

**Travel from I-57 Exit 40:**
Drive east about a half-mile and turn right (south) on Regent Lane.

Drive 1 mile on Regent Lane and park where Regent Creek crosses the road just upstream from waterfall. Don't ford stream.

**Safety Note:** Regent Lane is rough, one lane, with blind hills. Low clearance vehicles are warned. There are no guard rails where waterfall stream crosses road! Not safe for children. A rough trail without guard rails leads downstream from waterfall.

This waterfall is beside a rough gravel road at the west side of Ferne Clyffe State Park. Upstream, Regent Creek carved a channel into easily eroded Pennsylvanian shale, siltstone, and sandstone. The creek reaches resistant Pennsylvanian Caseyville sandstone and flows on top of this rock layer. At the eroded edge of the sandstone, water falls 36 feet. Sandstone slabs collapse from an alcove roof under the waterfall amphitheater (Figure 48).

Bork's Falls retreat is due to seepage erosion of groundwater moving through poorly-cemented sandstone to an exit under the resistant caprock (Figure 13).

The downstream box canyon is widened by seepage sapping. Groundwater seeps out of porous sandstone at the sandstone-shale boundary (Figures 46, 49). Bork's Falls began when the larger stream into which Regent's Creek flows eroded deep enough to cut through Caseyville sandstone. At this knickpoint the waterfall on Regent's Creek eroded weak shale (Figures 43, 44). The waterfall receded mainly by this mechanism until the stream bed ran only on sandstone (Figure 45). At this point, seepage erosion of sandstone took over (Figure 50).

References: Weibel and Nelson, 1993; Goreville topographic map; author's field data.

Figure 49: Blocks
fallen from bluffs
into Bork's Falls box
canyon. The result
of seepage erosion.

Figure 50: Regent Creek stream
profile (vertically exaggerated
to illustrate details). References:
Weibel and Nelson, 1993; Goreville
topographic map; author's field data.

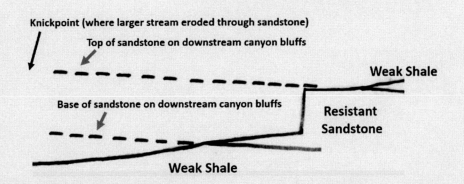

Knickpoint (where larger stream eroded through sandstone)

Top of sandstone on downstream canyon bluffs

Weak Shale

Base of sandstone on downstream canyon bluffs

Resistant
Sandstone

Weak Shale

37.5406, -88.9737

Happy Hollow Creek

# Ferne Clyffe Falls (Happy Hollow Falls)

Ferne Clyffe Falls is one of the most easily visited waterfalls in southern Illinois. It sits at the end of a box canyon and consists of a cascade, waterfall of 38 feet, and another cascade. The total drop to plunge pool is 67 feet. A large alcove is due to seepage erosion (Figure 51).

Happy Hollow Creek carved deeply into hills of easily eroded Pennsylvanian siltstone, shale, and poorly-cemented sandstone until it reached resistant Pennsylvanian Caseyville sandstone. The stream flowed over this sandstone until it reached a knickpoint, where it joined a larger stream that breached the sandstone and exposed shale underneath.

As in all Caseyville waterfalls, once the larger stream eroded deep enough to expose Caseyville sandstone and underlying shale, Happy Hollow Creek's waterfall began its journey upstream. Shale was removed by falling water, allowing the sandstone caprock to collapse (Figures 43, 44). This method of waterfall retreat persisted upstream until the stream channel no longer exposed shale. Waterfall retreat is now by seepage erosion (Figure 45). Downstream, sandstone blocks break away from canyon walls and slide on underlying soft shale (Figure 52). This seepage sapping widens the box canyon (Figure 46).

**Travel from I-24 Exit 7:** Drive west to IL-37; turn left (south) to Ferne Clyffe State Park.

**Travel from I-57 Exit 40:** Drive east to Goreville; turn right (south) to Ferne Clyffe State Park. Follow Park road to junction by Ferne Clyffe Lake, turn right to turnaround, park near restrooms. Take Big Rocky Hollow Trail (#4) at turnaround. Walking trail ¾ mile roundtrip to Falls.

**Safety Note:** A rough trail without guard rails leads downstream from waterfall. People have died by climbing waterfall or falling from cliff. Waterfalls are slick; never climb them. Stay on trails.

*References:* Weibel and Nelson, 1993; Goreville topographic map.

*Figure 51: Ferne Clyffe Falls. A poorly-cemented sandstone is sandwiched between well-cemented sandstones.*

*Figure 52: Seepage sapping releases sandstone to slide downhill.*

## Other Ferne Clyffe State Park waterfalls.

Travel: From turnaround, cross creek on stones, take right trail (Rebman Trail #1) ¼ mile to box canyon with waterfalls.

 37.5454, -88.9799

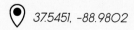 37.5451, -88.9802

37.5080, -88.6831

Tributary to East Branch of Cedar Creek

# Shawnee National Forest
## Cedar Falls
**(private property)**

Cedar Falls is one of the tallest and most beautiful waterfalls in Illinois. This picture-perfect waterfall has a free drop of 62 feet (Figure 53). Slabs fall from the alcove roof under the waterfall due to seepage erosion. Floods carry sand away from waterfall. The stream carved a canyon into easily eroded Pennsylvanian strata of shale, siltstone, and sandstone which overlie resistant Pennsylvanian Caseyville sandstone capping Cedar Falls. The waterfall was triggered where the tributary entered East Branch of Cedar Creek. East Branch eroded through the sandstone and exposed underlying weak shale. Niagara-style waterfall erosion washed weak shale from under the sandstone until the caprock broke off (Figures 43, 44). When the waterfall eroded only within the sandstone, retreat shifted to seepage erosion. The amphitheater, box canyon, and alcove with collapsed slabs are all evidences that seepage erosion is the main theme at Cedar Falls.

*Travel from I-24 Exit 14:* Drive northeast on US-45 to Ozark Road; turn right (east). In Ozark, turn right (south) at Camp Odossank. Visitors must request permission at main office.

**Safety Note:** Part of hiking trail is rough. Flash floods occur. Watch weather reports and inquire at Camp. Do not climb any waterfall. Compare videos below of Cedar Falls in 2015 and 2011:

youtu.be/xfSODJIZ-T8

youtu.be/U37UPla5VNg

*Reference:* Nelson and Lumm, 1990

**Figure 53**: Cedar Falls.
Slabs fell from alcove by seepage erosion.

37.5637, -88.6421

Burden Creek

# Burden Falls

There are several parts to this waterfall system:

An upper fall on the right side of the road: 2.5 ft. drop.

On the left side of the road are two drops of 2.5 and 9 feet. Small alcoves suggest groundwater seepage erosion.

The main waterfall has three drops totaling 35 feet. The largest free drop is 26 feet. Slabs fall from the waterfall front (Figure 54).

Below the main falls are perhaps 56 feet of small cascades and plunge pools (Figure 55. Accessibility made laser survey difficult. Downstream slabs are due to seepage sapping as sandstone broke from cliffs and slid downhill over wet shale. Total height from upper drop to lowest cascade is about 105 feet.

*Travel from I-24 Exit 14:* Drive northeast on US-45 to Ozark Road; rutn right (east); turn left onto Burdern Falls Road (McCormick Road), follow signs to Burden Falls. Road is rough with potholes. Park in lot on left side of road.

*Safety Note:* Burden Falls is popular to visit, but is very unsafe with no guard rails and slippery trails on canyon bluffs. Not recommended for children. People have died and been injured here.

Burden Creek carved a broad canyon through hills above the Falls into easily eroded Pennsylvanian shales, siltstones, and poorly-cemented sandstone. When the stream reached resistant Pennsylvanian Caseyville sandstone, the creek flowed on top of the sandstone. Not all layers erode equally which results in a series of waterfalls and cascades. The most resistant layer makes up the main waterfall. Below the sandstone is weak Pennsylvanian shale which grows vegetation and underlies low areas (Figure 55).

Burden Falls' history involved turbulence at the base of the main waterfall which removed underlying weak shale. This caused caprock sandstone to lose support, break off, and fall (Figures 43, 44). This Niagara-style process likely continues today. Large slabs in front of the main falls apparently fell from the waterfall (Figures 54, 55). Other slabs further downstream slid from canyon walls by seepage sapping (Figure 55).

**Figure 54**: Burden Falls. Main waterfall with collapsed blocks.

**Figure 55**: Burden Falls downstream from main waterfall. Slabs near falls due to Niagara-style recession; distant slabs slide downhill over shale due to seepage sapping on cliffs.

37.5080, -88.6831

*Tributary to Little Bay Creek*

**Travel from I-24 Exit 14:**
*Take US-45 northeast to Ozark Road; turn right (east); drive past Zion Church, turn right at Jackson Falls sign. Road is rough with potholes. Park in lot by restrooms.*

**Safety Note:** *Jackson Falls is popular but hazardous, e.g., no guard rails where trail crosses falls lip; unsafe for children. Flash floods have caused injuries here. Waterfalls are slick. Do not climb waterfalls.*

# Jackson Falls

The broad canyon upstream is carved in weak shales, siltstones, and poorly-cemented sandstones. Just upstream from Jackson Falls are small waterfalls and cascades. The stream runs on top of resistant Caseyville sandstone until water falls 24.5 feet to a plunge pool (Figure 56).

Jackson Falls displays evidence of Niagara-style waterfall retreat as seen in large blocks on either side of the waterfall (Figures 43, 44). This type of waterfall retreat has dominated the history of Jackson Falls. Turbulent erosion of shale below sandstone removed the sandstone's support and collapse occurred. This allowed waterfall retreat upstream.

There is also alcove development under the waterfall with small slabs that fell from the alcove roof. This suggests seepage erosion is also a factor in waterfall retreat.

It is unclear how waterfall retreat occurs in Jackson Falls. There is evidence of both Niagara-style waterfall collapse and seepage erosion. Jackson Falls may be at a transition between the two mechanisms of waterfall retreat. Further downstream, large slabs of sandstone broke from sides of the canyon by seepage sapping and slid downhill on wet shale. This widens the box canyon (Figure 57).

**Figure 57:** *Jackson Falls. Seepage sapping slabs slide downhill.*

**Reference:** *Nelson and Lumm, 1990*

*Figure 56:*
Jackson Falls.
Plunge pool and
collapsed slabs.

37.3867, -88.6687

💧 Artificial lake formed on a small stream

**Travel from I-24 Exit 14:** Drive east on IL-146 to Dixon Springs State Park. Watch oncoming traffic while turning left into the Park. Drive to parking lot. Walk to waterfall.

**Safety Note:** Rocky areas may favor poisonous snakes. Be careful around indentations and rock overhangs. Don't climb waterfalls.

# Dixon Springs State Park

Most Dixon Springs waterfalls are seen on a park trail after heavy rainfall. A waterfall is artificially formed as water issues from a dam and falls 12.5 feet. Downstream is a cascade dropping four feet (Figure 58). Pennsylvanian Caseyville sandstone blocks separate along joints and slide downhill (Figure 59).

**Figure 59:** Joint separation in Pennsylvanian Caseyville sandstone.

*References:* Wilson et al., 1966; Devera, 1991

*Figure 58*: Dixon Springs artificial waterfall and natural cascade.

# Mississippi River Bluffs

During the Pleistocene Ice Ages, glacial meltwater poured down the Mississippi River in huge volumes, carving a deep and wide channel. After glaciers melted away and river levels dropped, knickpoints developed where tributaries entered. Some knickpoints have waterfalls if resistant bedrock and adequate surface drainage are paired. Only a few waterfalls are on Illinois' western edge; some are on private property; others are in parks.

 37.7003, -89.4974

 Stream by Fountain Bluff Station

---

*Travel from IL-3/IL-149 Junction: Drive south; turn right (west) at the sign to Gorham.*

*Travel from IL-3/IL-146 Junction: Drive north; turn left (west) at the sign to Gorham.*

*At 2nd Street (second street on entering Gorham) turn left (south) to a small parking area on the left by the bluff.*

*Safety Note: One lane road is unpaved. Do not climb waterfall.*

## Fountain Bluff Station Falls (some of the area may be private property)

This waterfall is visible from the road and parking. Although small, the waterfall draws visitors. Long abandoned, this was a station on the Illinois Central Railroad. Archeologists recognize Native American petroglyphs on Fountain Bluff. Online examples are available at Peithmann (1955), and Frankie et al., (1999). Many are ruined by vandals. None are seen at the waterfall.

Pleistocene Ice Age meltwater eroded steep bluffs by the Mississippi River floodplain and isolated the large island called Fountain Bluff. A tributary stream eroded hills of weakly resistant Pennsylvanian sandstone, siltstone, and shale bedrock, forming a deep gorge (Figure 60). On reaching resistant Pennsylvanian Caseyville sandstone, surface water traveled along the top of the sandstone until it entered the Mississippi River floodplain as a waterfall (Figure 61). There has been little waterfall retreat since the river level dropped or erosion last cut into the bluff. Water drops a total of 15 feet. Alcoves layers suggest seepage erosion.

*References: Seid et al., 2009; Frankie et al., 1999.*

**Figure 60:** Stream valley carved into Fountain Bluff.

**Figure 61:** Fountain Bluff waterfall. Alcoves and resistant layers.

39.7873, -91.2968

Fall Creek

# Fall Creek Scenic Overlook Park Falls

**Travel from I-172 exit 2:**
*Turn right at stop sign onto IL-57; turn left at first road (N. 223rd Ln. or Payson Rd.); take first right to Fall Creek Scenic Overlook Park (at sign); park in lot by restrooms. Walk paved trail to wooden overlook of lower waterfall. Trail sign indicates rugged hiking to other waterfalls.*

**Safety Note:** *If visiting upper waterfalls, be alert for slippery slopes, wet conditions, and snakes. Do not climb waterfalls.*

This is an easy waterfall to visit. A lower waterfall drops 5 feet. Upstream waterfalls probably have drops less than 10 feet. A trail sign identifies bedrock as Mississippian Burlington Limestone. The lower waterfall is likely Mississippian sandstone caprock with weak shale underneath (Willman et al., 1975). The stream is unusual for Illinois since it traverses two different rock types and displays contrasting waterfall retreat processes. The upper waterfalls, with dense, blocky layers of limestone form sloping waterfalls being eroded by four methods:

| | |
|---|---|
| Solution (limestone is easily dissolved in water) by water running over the waterfall face. | Solution by water seeping into rock along limestone blocks. |
| Pressure from running water pushing on blocks. | Freezing water pushing blocks apart during winters. |

The similarity between this limestone waterfall and Rock Creek dolostone waterfall is striking. This illustrates the importance of rock type for waterfall shape since limestone and dolostone have similar physical properties. The lower waterfall (Figure 62) is similar to a Niagara-style waterfall. Resistant caprock over weak shale allows collapse of sandstone as shale is washed away.

**Figure 62**: Fall Creek lower waterfall. Sandstone over weak shale.

38.5307, -90.1854

Natural Spring

# Falling Springs Falls
**(Private Property)**

*Travel from I-255 southbound exit 9:* Turn left (east) at the stop sign; turn left onto Industrial Drive (frontage road).

*Travel from I-255 northbound exit 9:* At the stop sign, continue straight onto Industrial Drive (frontage road).

*Drive past a large limestone quarry; after a couple miles, road turns right (Falling Springs Drive). At the end of the street is a bluff with waterfall on private property. View only from public street.*

Falling Springs is unlike other waterfalls in this book; it is truly a spring (groundwater flows directly out of rock). The falls consists of two free drops of 20 and 30 feet, with a total of 50 feet to the floodplain floor (Figure 63). The spring emerges from Mississippian limestone. During Pleistocene Ice Ages, the Mississippi River carried huge volumes of glacial meltwater and eroded bluffs of Mississippian limestone. After meltwaters subsided, groundwater began to emerge about halfway down this eroded bluff. The spring is fed from the plateau behind the bluff. Rainwater flows into sinkholes and moves underground through openings dissolved by water (e.g., caves or fractures). Limestone is dissolved by groundwater. Water emerges from the bluff as a spring falling to the Mississippi River floodplain.

*Safety Note:* View waterfall from public street only. Watch for traffic. Do not attempt to enter property. Do not climb any waterfall.

*Figure 63:* Falling Springs Falls.

# References

Beisel, R.H. Jr, 2006, International Waterfall Classification System, Outskirts Press, 294 p.

Bruegger, A.R., 2016, Refining the span and rates of deposition of the Glenwood phase of Lake Chicago, M.S. thesis, University of Illinois at Urbana-Champaign.

Curry, B.B., E.R. Hajic, J.A. Clark, K.M. Befus, J.E. Carrell, and S.E. Brown, 2014, The Kankakee Torrent and other large meltwater flooding events during the last deglaciation, Illinois, USA, Quaternary Science Reviews, v. 90, p. 22-36.

Devera, J.A., 1991, Geologic Map of the Glendale Quadrangle, Pope and Johnson Counties, Illinois, IGQ Glendale-G: Illinois State Geological Survey.

Ford, D.C., 1968, Waterfalls in Geomorphology, Encyclopedia of Earth Science, Springer.

Frankie, W.T., 1997, Guide to the geology of Kankakee River State Park area, Kankakee, County, Illinois: Illinois State Geological Survey, Field Trip Guidebook 1997C, 62 p.

Frankie, W.T., 2004, Guide to the geology of Ferne Clyffe State Park and surrounding area, Johnson and Pope Counties, Illinois: Illinois State Geological Survey, Field Trip Guidebook 2004B, 49 p.

Frankie, Wayne T., R.J. Jacobson, C.A. Phillips, R.A. Locke, M.J. Wagner, 1998, Guide to the geology of the La Rue–Pine Hills area, Jackson and Union Counties, Illinois: Illinois State Geological Survey, Field Trip Guidebook 1998D, 87 p.

Gardner, T.W., 1983, Experimental study of knickpoint and longitudinal profile evolution in cohesive, homogeneous material, Geol. Soc. of America Bulletin, v. 94, p. 664-672.

Gilbert, G.K., 1895, Niagara Falls and their history, American Book Company, New York, Chicago, p. 203-236.

Illinois State Geological Survey, 2005, Time Talks: The geology of Starved Rock and Matthiessen State Parks: Illinois State Geological Survey, 50 p.

Irvine, M.C., 2001, Sandstone canyon development in Starved Rock State Park, Illinois, M.S. Thesis, Ball State University.

Kolata, D.R., et al., 2005, Bedrock geology of Illinois: Illinois Map 14, Illinois State Geological Survey.

Lamb, M.P., and W.D. Dietrich, 2009, The persistence of waterfalls in fractured rock. Geol. Soc. of America Bulletin, v.121 (7-8), p.1123–1134. doi: https://doi.org/10.1130/B26482.1

Lamb, M.P., A.D. Howard, J. Johnson, K.X. Whipple, W.E. Dietrich, and J.T. Perron, 2006, Can springs cut canyons into rock?, Jour. Geophysical Res., v. 111, E07002, doi:10.1029/2005JE002663.

Lobeck, A.K., 1939, Geomorphology, An introduction to the study of landscapes, McGraw-Hill Book Company, Inc., New York and London, 731 p.

Nelson, W.J. and D.K. Lumm, 1990, Geologic map of Stonefort Quadrangle: IGO 6, Illinois State Geological Survey.

Pasternack, G.B., C.R. Ellis, and J.D. Marr, 2007, Jet and hydraulic jump near-bed stresses below a horseshoe waterfall, Water Resour. Res., v. 43, W07449, doi:10.1029/2006WR005774

Peithmann, I., 1955, A petroglyph site at Fountain Bluff, Jackson County, Illinois, Central States Archaeological Jour., v. 2, No. 1, p. 11-13.

Reams, M.W., 2013, Geology of Illinois State Parks, Kindle, 141 p.

Reinertsen, D.L., M.M. Killey, P.C. Reed, and R.D. Brower, 1992, Guide to the geology of the Morris area: Grundy County and parts of Kankakee, Kendall, LaSalle, and Will Counties, Illinois: Illinois State Geological Survey Field Trip Guidebook 1992C, 45 p.

Sauer, C.O., G.H. Cady, H.C. Cowles, 1918, Starved Rock State Park and its environs, Geographical Society of Chicago Bulletin, No. 6, University of Chicago Press.

Scheingross, J.S., and M.P. Lamb, 2017, A mechanistic model of waterfall plunge pool erosion into bedrock, Jour. Geophysical Res.: Earth Surface, v. 122. https://doi.org/10.1002/2017JF004195

Shields, W.E., D.H. Malone, and B. Harp, 2005, Surficial geology of LaSalle Quadrangle, LaSalle County, Illinois: EDMAP (Illinois State University), Illinois State Geological Survey.

Thomas, J.T., T. Papanicolaou, C. Wilson, E.A. Bettis, and M. Elhakeem, 2018, Knickpoint migration in western Iowa streams, Geol. Soc. of America North-Central Section Meeting, Ames, Iowa, v. 50, n. 4, T21-3.

Thomason, J.F., 2003, Surficial geologic map, Starved Rock Quadrangle, LaSalle County, Illinois: EDMAP (Illinois State University), Illinois State Geological Survey.

Weibel, C.P., and R.S. Nelson, 2009, Geology of the Mackinaw River Watershed, McLean, Woodford, and Tazewell Counties, Illinois: Illinois State Geological Survey, Field Trip Guidebook 2009A, 48 p.

Willman, H.B., E. Atherton, T.C. Buschbach, C. Collinson, J.C. Frye, M.E. Hopkins, J.A. Lineback, and J.A. Simon, 1975, Handbook of Illinois stratigraphy: Illinois State Geological Survey Bulletin 95, 261 p.

Wilson, G.M., D.L. Reinertsen, and W. Cote, 1966, Guide to the geology of the Vienna area: Johnson and Massac Counties, Illinois: Illinois State Geological Survey Field Trip Guidebook 1966A, 17 p.

World Waterfall Database, www.worldwaterfalldatabase.com

Young, R.W., 2004, Waterfalls in Encyclopedia of Geomorphology, v. 1 & 2, A.S. Goudie (ed.), Routledge, Taylor & Francis Group, London and New York.

# Appendix

## Additional Waterfalls

If interested in other Illinois waterfalls, see online blogs, websites, etc. There are also artificial waterfalls on dams and other human constructions which can be found online. Always use caution and do not climb waterfalls.

## Waterfall definitions and classifications

For details about classification and measurement of waterfalls see: Ford (1968), World Waterfall Database (online), and Beisel (2006).

## Origins of Waterfalls

Waterfalls provide information about geologic events of the past. For information on causes of waterfalls see: Lobeck (1939).

## How Waterfalls Work

If interested in detailed theories of how waterfalls work, see any physical geology or geography or geomorphology textbook, especially featuring Gilbert's (1895) Niagara Falls model. Seepage erosion and seepage sapping models (Irvine, 2001) are described in this book. For other explanations see: Pasternack, et al (2007); Lamb, et al., (2006); Lamb, et al., (2009); Scheingross, et al., (2017).

## How fast do waterfalls retreat?

In addition to rates described in this book, see Young (2004): waterfall retreat rates vary widely, from 3,280 ft. per 1,000 years in Niagara and Victoria Falls, to 0.33 to 6.6 ft. per 1,000 years in southeast Australia.

We hope you enjoy the experience of visiting Illinois waterfalls. They are a generous gift from the Creator. Take your time and soak in the serene power of a waterfall.

Let worries and stress ebb away as you bask in the pleasure of listening and watching falling water. And, above all, practice safety during your visits.

*Carol A. Reams*

*Max W. Reams*

Made in the USA
Monee, IL
19 August 2021